A catalogue record for this book is available
from the British Library

Published by Ladybird Books Ltd Loughborough Leicestershire UK
Ladybird Books Ltd is a subsidiary of the Penguin Group of companies
LADYBIRD and the device of a Ladybird are trademarks of Ladybird Books Ltd

DISNEY'S

THE HUNCHBACK OF NOTRE DAME

Ladybird

High above Paris in the great cathedral of Notre Dame, lived a gentle young man called Quasimodo. Judge Frollo, who hated all gypsies, had been forced to look after him when he had caused the death of Quasimodo's gypsy mother twenty years earlier. Since then Frollo had hidden Quasimodo from the world in Notre Dame, telling him he would be rejected by everyone because of his ugliness. Quasimodo trusted his cruel master but longed to be part of the world outside.

It was the Festival of Fools, the most amazing festival of the year, and Quasimodo's only friends, three gargoyles called Hugo, Laverne and Victor, were excited. Quasimodo wanted to go but knew Frollo wouldn't allow it. Frollo had told Quasimodo that Notre Dame was the one place where he would be safe. "I'd never fit in out there," sighed Quasimodo. "I'm not… normal." But the gargoyles persuaded him to go.

Outside, a crowd watched a beautiful gypsy, Esmeralda, and her goat, Djali, dance. In the crowd was Phoebus, Frollo's new Captain of the Guard. His eyes met Esmeralda's and for a moment they gazed at each other. Suddenly, a gypsy whistled, warning that Frollo's guards were on their way. Esmeralda and Djali fled down an alley to hide.

As the crowd moved on, Phoebus reported for work where he learnt of Judge Frollo's hatred for the gypsies.

"They have a hideout in this very city – the Court of Miracles," Frollo said.

"What are we going to do about it, Sir?" asked Phoebus. In answer, Frollo angrily crushed a nest of ants.

Meanwhile, disguised in a hooded robe, Quasimodo swung down from the cathedral into the town square. The celebrations were well under way.

Quasimodo searched for a place to hide and accidentally fell into Esmeralda's dressing tent. "Are you hurt?" she asked. Quasimodo moved away, afraid that Esmeralda would make fun of his ugliness but she just smiled and said, "That's a great mask." Quasimodo now realised that he didn't need a disguise – he could join in the celebrations just as he was!

Soon it was time for the crowning of the King of Fools – the ugliest face in Paris. Frollo watched as people in masks gathered on the stage and Quasimodo was quickly pulled up to join them. Then Esmeralda removed each disguise in turn. When she reached Quasimodo she realised he *wasn't* wearing a mask. "It's the bell ringer from Notre Dame!" someone shouted. The crowd soon realised that Quasimodo would make the *perfect* king. He was given a crown and paraded through the streets by the cheering crowd.

However, the crowd began to tease Quasimodo and tied him up. "Please help me, Master," he begged Frollo. But Frollo wanted to punish Quasimodo for leaving Notre Dame, and ignored him. Esmeralda was the only one who tried to help.

Enraged at this, Frollo ordered the gypsy girl's immediate arrest.

Esmeralda and Djali ran into Notre Dame followed by Phoebus, Frollo and his guards. Phoebus, enchanted by Esmeralda, told Frollo that the gypsy girl had claimed sanctuary – this meant that no one could harm her while she was inside the cathedral. Furious, Frollo left with his guards. Phoebus smiled to himself, knowing that Esmeralda would be safe.

As Esmeralda explored the cathedral, she saw Quasimodo and followed him to his room. She spoke kindly to him, saying he was not the monster Frollo said he was.

Later, Quasimodo helped Esmeralda and Djali to escape. Before leaving, she gave her new friend a necklace with a map on it to help him find her. Frollo soon learnt of Esmeralda's escape and ordered his soldiers to search Paris for her…

Maddened by an unsuccessful search, Frollo set fire to a miller's home. Phoebus finally realised how truly evil Frollo was and bravely rescued the miller's family.

Frollo was angered by Phoebus' actions and ordered his immediate capture.

Esmeralda, who had been hiding nearby, suddenly ran forward and frightened Frollo's horse, causing a distraction – Phoebus tried to escape…

Frollo's soldiers took aim and fired. An arrow struck Phoebus and he fell, unconscious, into a river. Frollo, thinking he was dead, left him there. But Esmeralda rescued Phoebus and took him back to Notre Dame, where she begged Quasimodo to protect him from Frollo. Quasimodo now knew that Esmeralda loved Phoebus.

Suddenly, they heard Frollo's carriage pull up outside Notre Dame. Esmeralda turned to Quasimodo and said, "Promise me you won't let anything happen to Phoebus." Then she fled. Quasimodo quickly hid Phoebus under a table.

Frollo went to Quasimodo's room and sat at the table that hid Phoebus. He knew of Quasimodo's feelings for Esmeralda and guessed he could lead him to the Court of Miracles. Frollo began to put his plan into action. "I know where Esmeralda's hideout is," he lied to Quasimodo. "Tomorrow at dawn I will attack with a thousand men." Then he left, sure that Quasimodo would try to warn Esmeralda and so lead him straight to the gypsies' hideout.

Frollo was right! When Phoebus awoke, Quasimodo told him of Frollo's plan – they used the map on Esmeralda's necklace to find her. But once inside the hideout they were captured by the gypsies. The gypsy leader, believing they were Frollo's spies, wanted them hanged.

Suddenly, Esmeralda rushed forward. "Stop!" she cried. "These men are our friends! This soldier saved the miller's family and Quasimodo helped me escape from Notre Dame."

The gypsies realised Esmeralda was speaking the truth and listened as Phoebus and Quasimodo warned them of Frollo's attack. But Frollo and his men, who had followed Quasimodo and Phoebus, burst in on the gypsies! The soldiers took Phoebus, Esmeralda and the other gypsies away and chained Quasimodo up in Notre Dame.

That evening, Esmeralda was tied to a
stake in the town square. Phoebus, who was
now in prison, could do nothing to help.
Carrying a burning torch, Frollo walked
towards Esmeralda to light the fire…

High above, in the bell tower,
Quasimodo gathered all his strength and
broke free from his chains – he had to help
his friends. He quickly swung down from
the cathedral and rescued Esmeralda, who
had fainted. He then carried her back up
the face of Notre Dame.

"Seize the cathedral!" cried Frollo.

Inside Notre Dame, Quasimodo thought Esmeralda was dead and wept for the one true human friend he had ever had.

Walking out onto the balcony he saw Frollo's soldiers below. Overcome with anger, he threw wood and pieces of stone over the side – some of the soldiers fled.

Meanwhile, Phoebus had freed himself and the other gypsies. "Citizens of Paris," he cried. "Frollo has wronged our people, and now he has declared war on Notre Dame. Will we allow it?"

"No!" shouted the angry crowd.

A fierce battle followed...

Quasimodo fought off Frollo's soldiers by tipping a pot of molten lead over the cathedral's wall. The soldiers scattered but Frollo managed to enter Notre Dame. He found Quasimodo weeping over Esmeralda's body. "You killed her!" Quasimodo cried. "She was my friend."

"*I* am your only friend," Frollo replied. "Let us pray."

  As Quasimodo knelt, he saw Frollo raise
a dagger above his head. Quasimodo
managed to throw the dagger aside before
lifting Esmeralda, who had woken up, to
safety. A bitter struggle followed on the
balcony. Quasimodo and Frollo both lost
their balance but Esmeralda grabbed
Quasimodo's hand while Frollo fell to his
death. Soon Esmeralda could hold on to
Quasimodo no longer but luckily Phoebus
caught his faithful friend as he fell.

Next morning all the people of Paris gathered outside Notre Dame. The doors opened and Esmeralda and Phoebus walked out. Esmeralda beckoned to Quasimodo. The crowd were unsure of what to say or do until a young girl walked up to Quasimodo and gently touched his face. "Three cheers for Quasimodo!" someone cried.

Quasimodo smiled as he was carried through the streets – the new hero of Paris.